Oliver and Friends

Amazing things can happen when you're
Living the Beach Life

By Heidi Fagerberg

Edited by Carol Mitchell

About the author: Heidi holds degrees in Early Childhood Development, Education, and Human Services. She was born and raised in Irvington, New York. She has since lived in Delaware, Costa Rica and now has her home on St Kitts, a small island in the Caribbean. Currently she is working on additional books and developing project-based curriculum for the Living the Beach Life series. Throughout her life Heidi has been dedicated to caring for and educating the young and old alike. In 2008, she founded the St. Kitts Sailing School and during the time that the school was in operation she interacted with and cared for the characters in her books. She has taken a keen interest in orphaned animals and has adopted some of her own. Her love of photography and writing was rekindled by the beautiful island on which she lives and the animals that she loves. This has led her to create the series - Living the Beach Life.

About the Editor: Carol Mitchell is a professional editor, the founder of CaribbeanReads Publishing and the author of the Caribbean Adventure Series.

Photographs by Heidi Fagerberg
Also including photos by Jason Pereira and Lindsy Brockman.
Photo of glasses on page 26 by Belinda Pretorius/Shutterstock.com

CaribbeanReads Publishing, Washington DC, 20006
First Edition
© 2014 by CaribbeanReads Publishing
All rights reserved.
ISBN: 9780989930550

Remember me?

My name is Oliver and I grew up on the island of St. Kitts.

Two months old

One year old

Three years old

You may have read stories that Lion Paw and Wilbur shared. Now it's my turn to tell a story.

It's about a time when we were all together, living the beach life.

First there was Wilbur,

then there was Lion Paw,

and then there was me.

That made three.

And then there were four. Can you guess what animal came to live with us next?

It did not moo,

and it did not hop.

I'll give you more hints, if you still aren't sure.

It's called a kid when it is young and it stands on four furry legs.

Did you guess a goat? Then you were right!

It's Miss Mocha, the goat

Mocha, named for her light creamy brown color, came to us when she was a kid.

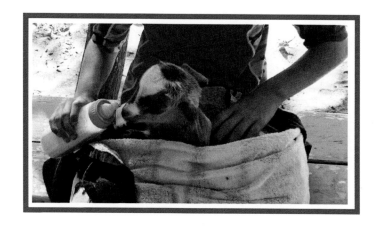

Our caretakers brought us together. They must have known that I would keep her safe.

We shared bottles. What a treat for me! Sweet milk yummy, yummy as can be!

Mocha grew quickly. Soon she ate what I ate. She loved bananas just like I do!

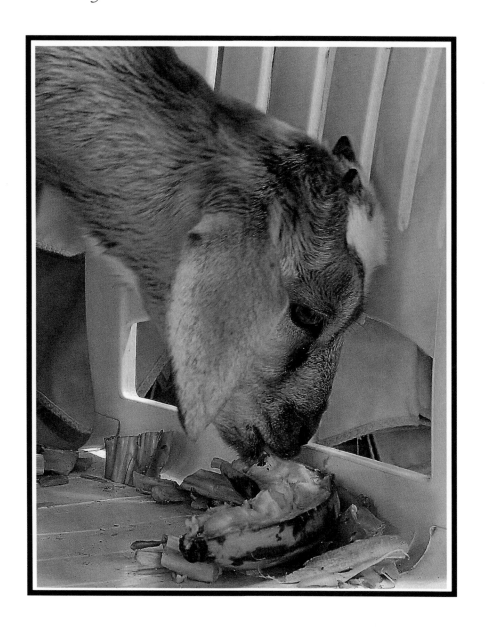

Then Mocha discovered that she loved leaves and would do whatever it took to reach them.

She didn't stop at eating leaves and bananas.
Mocha ate everything.

I mean EVERYTHING!

Mocha enjoying a newspaper

Sometimes Mocha would even nibble on the clothes of people who came to the beach.

This gave me the chance to do something very sneaky ...

While guests were distracted by Mocha's nibbling, I would quickly swipe their glasses.

As time went by, Mocha ate and ate and got bigger

...and bigger

...and bigger

Although getting bigger is normal for any kid, Mocha started feeling cramped in our little home.

Our caretakers moved Mocha to a nearby hillside.

There was space for her to roam and tons of grass for her to graze.

But the move did NOT go well!

Mocha and I did not like being separated so we refused to eat.

Our caretakers even tried giving us our favorite foods.

Pineapple

Coconuts

We still didn't eat.

They had no choice, but to return Mocha to our home.

We were still too cramped so they tried letting us spend time on the beach together.

Mocha could stretch her legs.
We were happy, but this did not work either!

I got into people's things and

Mocha still ate everything including things that were NOT hers to eat.

Our caretakers did not give up.

They came up with a new idea and this time they got it right. *A fenced area around my cage.*

The perfect solution!

How happy Mocha was in her new little space.

The best part about this new space for me was ...

Mocha sunbathing in her favorite spot

Mocha had more access to unsuspecting guests, and ...

Mocha looking for our next target

My game of swiping glasses became so much easier.

Our caretakers took to warning everyone.

"Watch out for your glasses!"

Pair One, YES!

But people were so busy stopping Mocha from chewing their clothes that they didn't hear the warnings.

Another pair for me

More than 100 pairs of glasses were retrieved over the next few years.

My record was 22 pairs in one day! I couldn't have done that without Mocha's help.

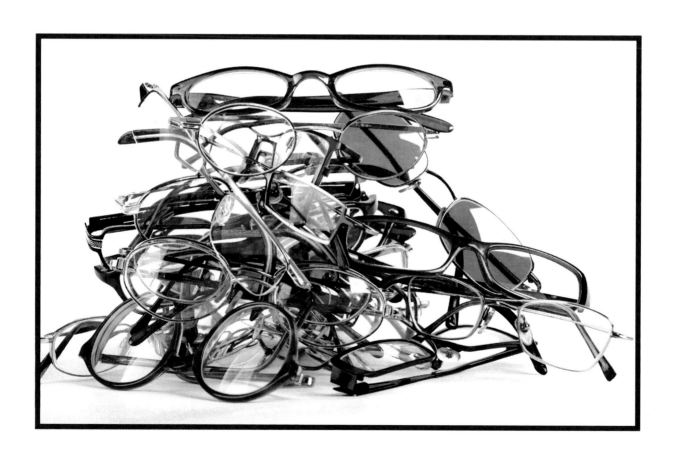

My friends and I have really had so much fun Living the Beach Life on St Kitts.

CPSIA information can be obtained
at www.ICGtesting.com
Printed in the USA
404631LV00002B/6